"The Men Will Fear You, and the Women Will Adore You"

by

William Hamilton

The New Yorker cartoonist

St. Martin's Press
New York

Design by Doris Borowsky

Library of Congress Cataloging in Publication Data

Hamilton, William, 1939–
The men will fear you, and the women will adore you.

I. Title.
PS3558.A4444M4 1986 741.5'973 86-3720
ISBN 0-312-52965-1 (pbk.)

First Edition
10 9 8 7 6 5 4 3 2 1

“Bankers’ Faces, Everybody”

"What do you do?"

"I'm a lawyer."
"The law."
"I do law."
"I practice law."
"I'm an attorney."
"Something legal."

"Hey—bankers' faces, everybody—it's ten o'clock, the bank's open."

"We bought your cement company, Mr. Timkin, not your whimsy."

"We've got to give the appearance of changing direction without giving the appearance of changing principles in a way that won't be dismissed as cosmetic."

"You, sir, were my hero—until I became my own hero."

"You promised me the company on my sixtieth—and I don't think you're being a very nice daddy and I hate you."

"Say, where's that knowing little smile of the insider?"

"I want more than a slogan—I want an aphorism!"

"Oh, admit it, Tom—the only reason we merged was because everyone was merging."

"Oh, I've had some nice things said about me, but I've never been—you know—hailed."

"Miss Watson, what the hell is falafel?"

"I'll have the businessman's lunch, Philippe, and bring my son here the freelancer's lunch."

"I got in on the ground floor—and I stayed there."

"Apres us, the deluge!"

"Call me old-fashioned, but I like the way kids are thinking money again."

"Miss White, I thought I told you never to put through anyone who said they wanted to share something with me."

"Sir, there are certain perks we consider inalienable perks."

"We are being wooed."

"Only doubts about his masculinity kept him from openly crying."

"Call me Tom. Perhaps, in time, I'll let you call me Skippy."

"Sorry. For a minute there I was daydreaming of jug wine and flowers and the Quicksilver Messenger Service."

"How about one of those sunny old grandpas who make things look honest?"

"We've shown them we can take the heat. Now let's show them we can take the humidity, too."

"Is that still my possible successor or has he succeeded?"

"Not all the news is bad. Research indicated U.S. Steel would do extremely well as the name of a male fragrance."

"Don't knock it. We're very excited about nuclear waste."

"Young Mr. Dodds here is our first round draft choice from Stanford Business School."

"Now ask yourself—did you really want this acquisition, or are you just on the rebound?"

"Excuse me, sir, but I forgot which parable we quote when the stockholders start screaming."

"Look—I didn't start out to become a volatile executive—I also thought about being a temperamental actor or a high-strung musician."

"Look, Mom—can I get back to you? I happen to be on a roll."

"The image we're going to create for you is that of a man who doesn't give a hoot about his image."

"A Super Nice Time of Life"

"What's this new little thing of swearing in French?"

"No, I don't want to work on my anger with you. I want to pop you one!"

"Oh, great! You've failed me emotionally and now you want me to wash the dishes!"

"Gossip should be declared a medium."

"Nothing has really happened for him, so he's decided to become a character."

"Hey, now, don't get upset. I know we agreed not to call, but I couldn't resist when I saw our little restaurant listed in the 'Times' with a health-code violation."

"It's about scallops and snapper and dill, but I think what's different about it is it's also about sturgeon."

"Fiction's nice, but it doesn't get you anywhere."

"I am sick of being looked at like one of your Brazilian bank loans!"

"We had no idea you guys were wealthy."

"We're so depressed! We thought we were going to one of those really happy, pretty Scandinavian movies, but it turned out to be one of those grim, wildly unhappy Scandinavian movies."

"Well, tonight wasn't all bad. At least, this awful friendship finally bottomed out."

"He <u>was</u> Whitmanesque. He was wonderful! Then he started becoming Kafkaesque."

"It's for me. I can tell that cute little stockbroker's ring."

“Thanks, Helen—actually, I think we’re both delightfully American.”

"I just don't know if I'm ready to combine incomes with anybody at this point, Freddy."

"Ever get the feeling you're being groomed for mediocrity?"

"Do you realize we are living through the second time people got tired of Art Deco?"

"Now that Ted's executive vice president, we've decided from now on to always include his middle name."

"She's not here at the moment. You might try her work situation."

"If that's too much, we also have it both in authentic reproduction and cheap knock-off."

"We're all pretty tense. My father is a takeover target."

"Honestly, I think the only thing you have to fear about this look is fear itself."

"Jane Fonda has made money out of every stage of my life."

"I think it's a super nice time of life, the kids away at school and Tom having too much money to divorce me."

"I love the technology of your shoes."

"The Men Will Fear You, and the Women Will Adore You"

"Now, for God's sake don't start telling everyone how little we paid for everything."

"The Sculleys, the Jensons, the Walkers, Freddy, Joan, Don, and the Bowes. Oh, well, Madame de Staël had to start somewhere."

"It's a completely unspoiled country. You don't even see any jogging."

"You have a very, very funny bathroom!"

"Merry Christmas, folks. And I want to say I couldn't be president of this great company without the support of each and every one of you, or people very much like you."

"And now, after all the Chateau Hoo-Hoo and the Chateau Boo-Boo, we try the Chateau Coo-Coo!"

"We decided to just stay preppy, as though nothing had happened."

"Alex is just a flag of convenience."

"I wasn't talking about those sixties, I was talking about my sixties."

"I may be giving out, but I'm not giving in."

"You're right, Margo. You are hearing a lot of pain. Happily, though, it's coming from these damned shoes."

"This is Courtney, who changed my mind about growing old gracefully."

"Oh dear, the bow tie type."

"Don't you see, Herb? The seventies are over, we are over, even that dumb mustache of yours is over."

"She's really old-fashioned. She lets you pay for everything."

"Ted, I love the way you make drinking seem so damned effortless."

"So this is Charlie's little cash cow!"

"Oh nonsense, Allen, my father went through far more money than your father."

"Thanks—once in a while it's kind of a relief to just be superficial."

"That is beautiful, Scott. Did you make it up, or is it a bromide?"

"Maine? What an authentic place to come from."

"I couldn't agree more—China is going to be a very big thing."

"Bob, parties aren't the place for insights."

"I made my money the old-fashioned way—I inherited it."

"Look—our cowboy boots! Can you believe we ever wore cowboy boots?"

"This is my kind of deal—we're paying back everybody we owe and getting rid of this Cotes De Rhone."

"Great fun! I love talking about how we hate these things."

"I don't see why you don't like going to the Wentworths. It's true she refused to marry me, but that was twenty years ago, and in the meantime, I've crushed him in business."

"Now, brighten up. You know you'll have fun. The men will fear you, and the women will adore you."